This is Thumper.

His parents named him Thumper because
he thumps his foot when he's thinking.

He thumps his foot when he's surprised.

He even thumps his foot when he
wants to wake someone up!

Match each Thumper to his shadow.

Thumper lives in the forest with his
mother and his father...

...and his four little sisters.
That's right, four sisters!

Sometimes, having so many
sisters can be a pain.

But most of the time they have fun together.
Circle the 4 things that do not belong in this picture.

As Thumper's father always says,
"The family that plays together, stays together."

This is Thumper's sister Trixie.
She likes to go on adventures.

This is Daisy. She has lots of energy.

This is Ria. She is supersmart.

Last but not least is little Tessie.
She is crazy about her big brother.

Tessie follows Thumper everywhere.
How many Ts do you find?

Your answer:

Sometimes, Thumper pretends not to notice Tessie.
But never for long!

Thumper knows how lucky
he is to have such a great family.

There's so much to see and do in the forest every day.

Circle 4 things you find in the picture
that start with the letter S.

Wake up, sleepyheads!

It's time to start the day!

It's time for breakfast!

Mmm! The bunnies love clover.

Mama Bunny sees that Thumper is only eating the flowers.
"Remember what your father says," she tells him.

"Eating greens is a special treat. It makes
long ears and great big feet," Thumper recites.
"But it sure is awful stuff to eat!" he whispers.

After breakfast, it's time to play.

The bunnies begin a game of hide-and-seek.

Can you help Thumper find his sisters?
Circle them.

Answers: The bunnies are in the log, behind the stump, behind the rock, and in the clover.

Thumper and his sisters love to race.
"Last one across the log is a rotten egg!" calls Daisy.

Sometimes, when they feel like being nice, the bunnies let little Tessie win. (But they don't tell her that.)

Winning makes Tessie very happy.

It's always fun to go turtle hopping at the pond.

The turtles don't seem to mind—very much, that is!

Oops! Thumper slipped!

What did the turtle say to Thumper?
To find out, begin at START and write the letters
on the lines below in the order that they appear.

____ ____ ____ __ , ____

____ ____ __ !

Once Thumper has dried off,
Daisy suggests a game of leapfrog.

Whew! The bunnies are tired.
It's time for a rest.

After their nap, Daisy has an idea.
"Let's visit our friends," she says.

The bunnies have lots of friends in the forest.
Here are Mrs. Opossum and her children,
who like to just hang around.

Friend Owl is very wise and likes to give advice.

Circle 6 things that are different between the two pages.

Don't be surprised if Friend Owl turns his
head backward. He's good at it!

The squirrel and the chipmunk live in
Friend Owl's tree.

Here comes Mrs. Quail with her nine babies.

Mr. Mole pops up when you least expect it!

Mr. Mole has dug so many tunnels that he's lost!
Help him find his way to the pond.

Answer: C

This is Flower. He is a special friend.

Thumper and his sisters know never to sneak up on a skunk.
When they forget, they get a *very* stinky surprise!

Friends come in all shapes and sizes!

Some friends are so small they can wash
their faces with a dewdrop!

After a day in the forest, it's time to go home.
Help the bunnies find their way.

Start

Finish

There's nothing nicer than a bedtime story
before drifting off to sleep.

Papa Bunny tells a story about a brave bunny
who has many adventures.

Goodnight, bunnies!

What do bunnies dream about?

Every season is different in the forest.
Can you match the name of the season with the picture?

winter   spring   summer   fall

Answers: 1-summer, 2-spring, 3-winter, 4-fall.

During the summer,
the bunnies love to sit in the sun.

It's fun to find shapes in the clouds.

What do you see?

Daisy loves ladybugs! How many do you count?

Your answer:

The bunnies like to visit the pond.
The ducks swim by, all in a row.

Frogs enjoy jumping, just like bunnies!

Dragonflies may look dangerous,
but they don't sting.

But bees can sting!
The bunnies know they need to be careful.

"Time to chase butterflies!" says Trixie.

Circle the butterfly that is different.

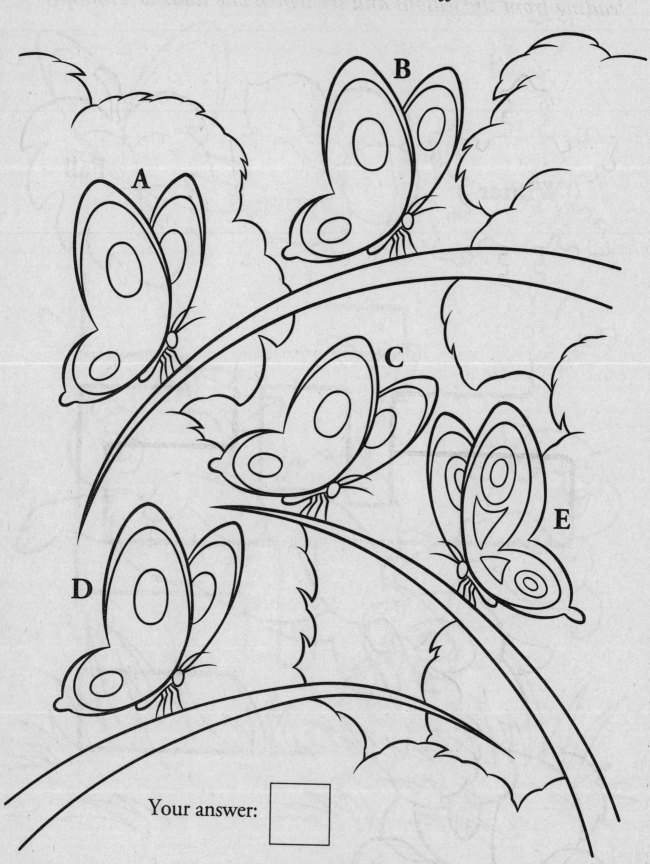

Your answer: ☐

Which season comes after summer? To find out, trace the lines leading from the seasons and see which one leads to Thumper.

Winter

Spring

Fall

Color the leaves red, orange, and yellow.

Ria loves the pretty leaves.
Which leaf matches the one she is holding?

A

B

C

D

Tessie finds something fun—a seesaw!

But when Trixie hops off, Thumper goes down!

Thumper isn't hurt. He laughs and laughs.

The forest animals start to prepare for the winter.
Squirrels collect nuts.

Some birds fly south.

The leaves begin to fall.
Thumper loves to jump into piles of leaves.

© 2010 Disney

Which season comes after fall?
Unscramble the letters below to find out.

I R W N E T

____ ____ ____ ____ ____ ____

Answer: WINTER

Brrr! It's winter! That's when some of the animals hibernate.
"See you in the spring!" says Flower.

Thumper and his sisters miss their hibernating friends.
But there's so much to do in winter!
Look, there's the first snowfall!

Draw lines between the snowflakes that match.

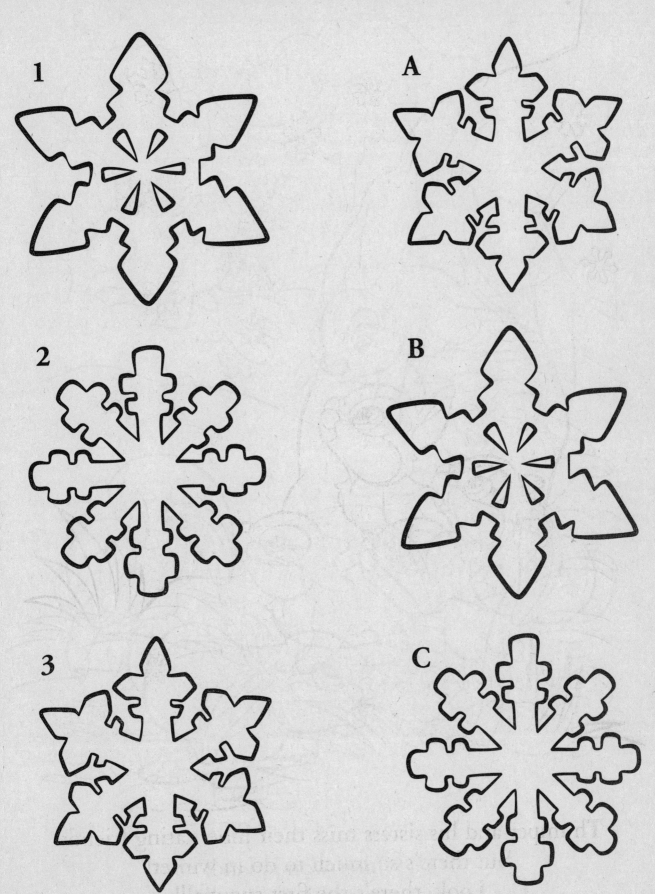

It's a winter wonderland!
The bunnies run and jump in the snow.

Watch out, Thumper!

There's nothing colder than two ears full of snow!

The animals snuggle together to stay warm.

Thumper teaches his sisters how to skate on the ice.

Wheee!

Tessie falls, but she gets right back up.

The bunnies see something.
Connect the dots to find out what it is.

Your answer: _____

One day Thumper discovers something and tells his sisters.
To find out what he says, begin at the arrow and write the letters
on the blanks in the order in which they appear.

___ ___ ___ ___ ___ ___

___ ___ ___ ___ •

The bunnies are glad the birds are back.
Circle the one that is different.

Your answer: [ ]

The sleeping animals wake up.

Lots of baby animals are born in the spring.
Can you match the mothers with their babies?

It rains a lot in the spring! Mushrooms make
good umbrellas—if you're a mouse, that is.

Flowers bloom in the spring.
Flower loves flowers!

There's nothing quite as cheerful...

...as a big, beautiful rainbow.

"Come play!"